BIRDS OF A FEATHER

by willi baum

▲▼ addison-wesley

An Addisonian Press Book

The Addison-Wesley Publishing Company, Inc., Reading, Massachusetts
Library of Congress catalog card number 76–88685
Printed in the United States of America
First Printing

for little jacqueline

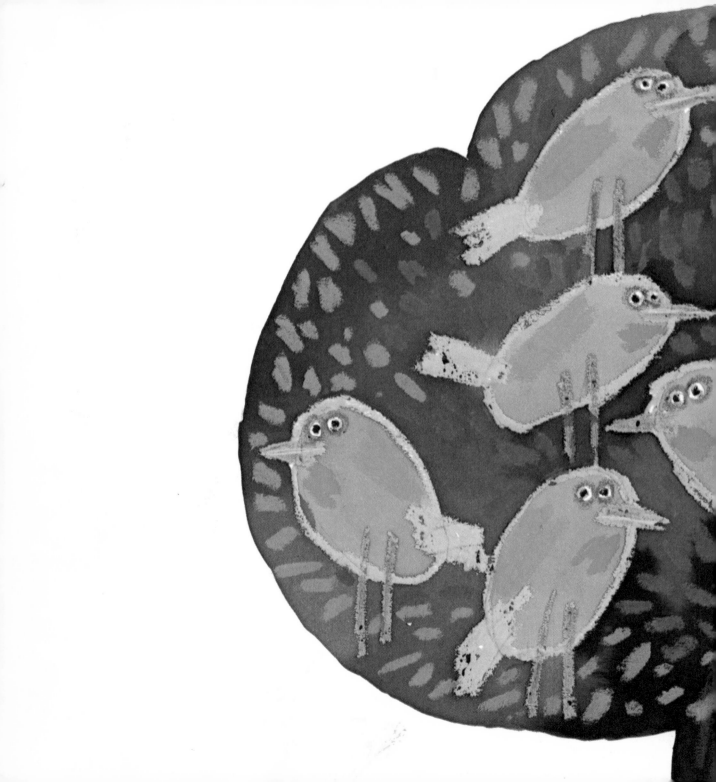